Francis Frith's

WINDMILLS & WATERMILLS

PHOTOGRAPHIC MEMORIES

Francis Frith's

WINDMILLS
& WATERMILLS

Anthony Bryan

First published in the United Kingdom in 2000 by
The Francis Frith Collection®

This edition published in 2006 by Bounty Books,
a division of Octopus Publishing Group,
2-4 Heron Quays, London E14 4JP, England

ISBN-13: 9780753714041
ISBN-10: 0-7537-1404-3

British Library Cataloguing in Publication Data

Windmills & Watermills
Anthony Bryan
ISBN 0-7537-1404-3

The Francis Frith Collection®
Frith's Barn, Teffont,
Salisbury, Wiltshire SP3 5QP
Tel: +44 (0) 1722 716 376
Email: info@francisfrith.co.uk
www.francisfrith.com

Printed in England

Front Cover: HORSTEAD, *The Mill 1902* 48149p

*The colour-tinting is for illustrative purposes only, and is not intended
to be historically accurate*

Every attempt has been made to contact copyright holders of illustrative material.
We will be happy to give full acknowledgement in future editions for any items not credited.
Any information should be directed to The Francis Frith Collection®

AS WITH ANY HISTORICAL DATABASE THE FRITH ARCHIVE IS CONSTANTLY BEING CORRECTED AND IMPROVED
AND THE PUBLISHERS WOULD WELCOME INFORMATION ON OMISSIONS OR INACCURACIES

Contents

Francis Frith: *Victorian Pioneer*

FRANCIS FRITH, Victorian founder of the world-famous photographic archive, was a complex and multi-talented man. A devout Quaker and a highly successful Victorian businessman, he was both philosophic by nature and pioneering in outlook.

By 1855 Francis Frith had already established a wholesale grocery business in Liverpool, and sold it for the astonishing sum of £200,000, which is the equivalent today of over £15,000,000. Now a very rich man, he was able to indulge his passion for travel. As a child he had pored over travel books written by early explorers, and his fancy and imagination had been stirred by family holidays to the sublime mountain regions of Wales and Scotland. 'What a land of spirit-stirring and enriching scenes and places!' he had written. He was to return to these scenes of grandeur in later years to 'recapture the thousands of vivid and tender memories', but with a different purpose. Now in his thirties, and captivated by the new science of photography, Frith set out on a series of pioneering journeys to the Nile regions that occupied him from 1856 until 1860.

Intrigue and Adventure

He took with him on his travels a specially-designed wicker carriage that acted as both dark-room and sleeping chamber. These far-flung journeys were packed with intrigue and adventure. In his life story, written when he was sixty-three, Frith tells of being held captive by bandits, and of fighting 'an awful midnight battle to the very point of surrender with a deadly pack of hungry, wild dogs'. Sporting flowing Arab costume, Frith arrived at Akaba by camel sixty years before Lawrence, where he encountered 'desert princes and rival sheikhs, blazing with jewel-hilted swords'.

During these extraordinary adventures he was assiduously exploring the desert regions bordering the Nile and patiently recording the antiquities and peoples with his camera. He was the first photographer to venture beyond the sixth cataract. Africa was still the mysterious 'Dark Continent', and Stanley and Livingstone's historic meeting was a decade into the future. The conditions for picture taking confound belief. He laboured for hours in his wicker dark-room in the sweltering heat of the desert, while the volatile chemicals fizzed dangerously in their trays. Often he was forced to work in remote tombs and caves where conditions were cooler. Back in London he exhibited his photographs and was

'rapturously cheered' by members of the Royal Society. His reputation as a photographer was made overnight. An eminent modern historian has likened their impact on the population of the time to that on our own generation of the first photographs taken on the surface of the moon.

Venture of a Life-Time

Characteristically, Frith quickly spotted the opportunity to create a new business as a specialist publisher of photographs. He lived in an era of immense and sometimes violent change. For the poor, in the early part of Victoria's reign, work was a drudge and the hours long, and people had precious little free time to enjoy themselves. Most had no transport other than a cart or gig at their disposal, and had not travelled far beyond

the boundaries of their own town or village. However, by the 1870s, the railways had threaded their way across the country, and Bank Holidays and half-day Saturdays had been made obligatory by Act of Parliament. All of a sudden the ordinary working man and his family were able to enjoy days out and see a little more of the world.

With characteristic business acumen, Francis Frith foresaw that these new tourists would enjoy having souvenirs to commemorate their days out. In 1860 he married Mary Ann Rosling and set out with the intention of photographing every city, town and village in Britain. For the next thirty years he travelled the country by train and by pony and trap, producing fine photographs of seaside resorts and beauty spots that were keenly bought by millions of Victorians. These prints were painstakingly pasted into family albums and pored over during the dark nights of winter, rekindling precious memories of summer excursions.

The Rise of Frith & Co

Frith's studio was soon supplying retail shops all over the country. To meet the demand he gathered about him a small team of photographers, and published the work of independent artist-photographers of the calibre of Roger Fenton and Francis Bedford. In order to gain some understanding of the scale of Frith's business one only has to look at the catalogue issued by Frith & Co in 1886: it runs to some 670 pages, listing not only many thousands of views of the British Isles but also many photographs of most European countries, and China, Japan, the USA and

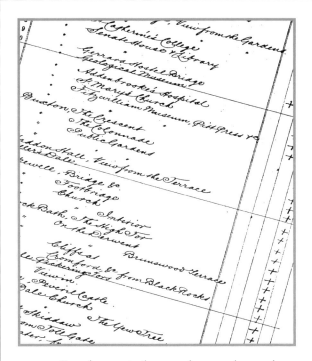

Canada – note the sample page shown above from the hand-written *Frith & Co* ledgers detailing pictures taken. By 1890 Frith had created the greatest specialist photographic publishing company in the world, with over 2,000 outlets – more than the combined number that Boots and W H Smith have today! The picture on the right shows the *Frith & Co* display board at Ingleton in the Yorkshire Dales (left of window). Beautifully constructed with a mahogany frame and gilt inserts, it could display up to a dozen local scenes.

Postcard Bonanza

The ever-popular holiday postcard we know today took many years to develop. In 1870 the Post Office issued the first plain cards, with a pre-printed stamp on one face. In 1894 they allowed other publishers' cards to be sent through the mail with an attached adhesive halfpenny stamp. Demand grew rapidly, and

in 1895 a new size of postcard was permitted called the court card, but there was little room for illustration. In 1899, a year after Frith's death, a new card measuring 5.5 x 3.5 inches became the standard format, but it was not until 1902 that the divided back came into being, with address and message on one face and a full-size illustration on the other. *Frith & Co* were in the vanguard of postcard development, and Frith's sons Eustace and Cyril continued their father's monumental task, expanding the number of views offered to the public and recording more and more places in Britain, as the coasts and countryside were opened up to mass travel.

Francis Frith died in 1898 at his villa in Cannes, his great project still growing. The archive he created continued in business for another seventy years. By 1970 it contained over a third of a million pictures of 7,000 cities, towns and villages. The massive photographic record Frith has left to us stands as a living monument to a special and very remarkable man.

Frith's Archive: *A Unique Legacy*

FRANCIS FRITH'S legacy to us today is of immense significance and value, for the magnificent archive of evocative photographs he created provides a unique record of change in 7,000 cities, towns and villages throughout Britain over a century and more. Frith and his fellow studio photographers revisited locations many times down the years to update their views, compiling for us an enthralling and colourful pageant of British life and character.

We tend to think of Frith's sepia views of Britain as nostalgic, for most of us use them to conjure up memories of places in our own lives with which we have family associations. It often makes us forget that to Francis Frith they were records of daily life as it was actually being lived in the cities, towns and villages of his day. The Victorian age was one of great and often bewildering change for ordinary people,

See Frith at www.francisfrith.co.uk

and though the pictures evoke an impression of slower times, life was as busy and hectic as it is today.

We are fortunate that Frith was a photographer of the people, dedicated to recording the minutiae of everyday life. For it is this sheer wealth of visual data, the painstaking chronicle of changes in dress, transport, street layouts, buildings, housing, engineering and landscape that captivates us so much today. His remarkable images offer us a powerful link with the past and with the lives of our ancestors.

Today's Technology

Computers have now made it possible for Frith's many thousands of images to be accessed almost instantly. In the Frith archive today, each photograph is carefully 'digitised' then stored on a CD Rom. Frith archivists can locate a single photograph amongst thousands within seconds. Views can be catalogued and sorted under a variety of categories of place and content to the immediate benefit of researchers.

Inexpensive reference prints can be created for them at the touch of a mouse button, and a wide range of books and other printed materials assembled and published for a wider, more general readership. The day-to-day workings of the archive are very different from how they were in Francis Frith's time: imagine the herculean task of sorting through eleven tons of glass negatives as Frith had to do to locate a particular sequence of pictures! Yet the archive still prides itself on maintaining the same high standards of excellence laid down by Francis Frith, including the painstaking cataloguing and indexing of every view.

It is curious to reflect on how the internet now allows researchers in America and elsewhere greater instant access to the archive than Frith himself ever enjoyed. Many thousands of individual views can be called up on screen within seconds on one of the Frith internet sites, enabling people living continents away to revisit the streets of their ancestral home town, or view places in Britain where they have enjoyed holidays. Many overseas researchers welcome the chance to view special theme selections, such as transport, sports, costume and ancient monuments.

We are certain that Francis Frith would have heartily approved of these modern developments in imaging techniques, for he himself was always working at the very limits of Victorian photographic technology.

The Value of the Archive Today

Because of the benefits brought by the computer, Frith's images are increasingly studied by social historians, by researchers into genealogy and ancestory, by architects, town planners, and by teachers and schoolchildren involved in local history projects.

In addition, the archive offers every one of us an opportunity to examine the places where we and our families have lived and worked down the years. Highly successful in Frith's own era, the archive is now, a century and more on, entering a new phase of popularity.

The Past in Tune with the Future

Historians consider the Francis Frith Collection to be of prime national importance. It is the only archive of its kind remaining in private ownership and has been valued at a million pounds. However, this figure is now rapidly increasing as digital technology enables more and more people around the world to enjoy its benefits.

Francis Frith's archive is now housed in an historic timber barn in the beautiful village of Teffont in Wiltshire. Its founder would not recognize the archive office as it is today. In place of the many thousands of dusty boxes containing glass plate negatives and an all-pervading odour of photographic chemicals, there are now ranks of computer screens. He would be amazed to watch his images travelling round the world at unimaginable speeds through network and internet lines.

The archive's future is both bright and exciting. Francis Frith, with his unshakeable belief in making photographs available to the greatest number of people, would undoubtedly approve of what is being done today with his lifetime's work. His photographs, depicting our shared past, are now bringing pleasure and enlightenment to millions around the world a century and more after his death.

Watermills & Windmills

THE POPULATION OF Britain has exploited natural power sources for thousands of years. There was a practical and economic need to utilise power sources greater than those provided by human limbs or the harnessing of domesticated animals. This led to the need to exploit natural, self-renewing power sources. The use of wind and waterpower began when technical knowledge and construction skills had advanced sufficiently to achieve success. Wind and waterpower resources are distributed throughout Britain; the need to exploit them grew as the population numbers and density increased, particularly in and near to towns. Our pictures show mills from all regions of Britain located both in the country and in towns. Most mills traded as a business, so economics were an important factor in their success. This influenced the type and construction of mechanical mills and their development and trade.

Water Power

Water is a finite, reliable and potentially very large power source, which was widely exploited throughout Britain. Today, many water resources are needed for public water supply, but this was not the situation three hundred years ago when watermills were in their heyday. Waterpower is usually dependent on rainfall, but flooding is a problem which can temporarily put watermills out of action and cause damage to stock and premises. Another source of waterpower is the tide mill, which is carefully sited to store and use the energy created by tidal variations in sea

level. Watermills have been evolving for at least 2000 years, and a wide variety of examples are included in the pictures. Some of our pictures show transport at the mill, usually for the miller or a customer - sometimes a cart or a boat, or in later years a motor vehicle. Watermills were often built alongside navigable rivers, and could take advantage of efficient bulk transport in a barge or perhaps an even smaller craft. A barge could carry tens of tons of grain in sacks at low cost, giving the miller a price advantage. In the same way, the flour produced by such a mill could be easily delivered to a customer requiring large quantities, at similarly low cost. Generally, mills sited near to the heads of navigable waterways were large and prosperous owing to the economic advantages of their siting.

Watermills were usually constructed of local building materials, and reflect the prosperity of an area in the late 19th century. The buildings contained very active businesses, which caused considerable wear and tear, and structural and mechanical reconstruction usually occurred every fifty years or so. Both the mill building and its machinery were inextricably linked to the milling process. A mill is part building and part machine, and the two functions are inseparable. Mill buildings have distinctive features such as height, lucams, lanterns and roof ventilators. A building about three stories high, with water channels passing underneath or alongside, indicates to an observer that it could be a watermill. Our photographs show a wide variety of picturesque watermill locations; they range from the remote and very rural to those in thriving towns. Some are next to ponds, others beside rivers or on shorelines.

Waterwheels

The easiest way to exploit waterpower is by the use of a waterwheel. Early waterwheels were largely made of wood; they were constructed by local craftsmen, who were often noted characters. Later, after 1850, waterwheels were made of iron, as castings became available at reasonable cost. Wooden waterwheels needed a lot of expensive maintenance, and would require renewing every 25 years or so owing to wear and tear and timber rot. Iron waterwheels could last for about 100 years with low maintenance. This is why many surviving examples of waterwheels are often made of iron. Waterwheels were located outside or inside buildings; if outside, they sometimes had a roof or protective covering. There was a need to protect waterwheels from icing in winter and from high winds, which could rob the wheel of power or blow water out of the buckets. Splashing water could be a wasteful nuisance if not contained.

Wind Power

Wind is an infinite renewable power source; it is unreliable and difficult to exploit, and can be very destructive. Windmills are easily damaged by strong winds, and are expensive to repair. Windmills were often built in remote places, either in flatlands or on hilltops and ridges, so access roads could be long and steep or muddy, and only light loads could be carried by wheeled carts on primitive roads. Pack animals could carry even less.

Windmills

Windmills were introduced into Britain around the 14th century, when technology had advanced sufficiently to construct powerful, and reliable, mills. Examples of mills built in the 19th century are shown in the pictures. Windmills usually feature the local designs of their constructors, and the materials available in the locality. Constructional detail tended to vary regionally owing to the favourite ideas of local craftsmen and their customers, the mill owners. Thus the windmills of the north-east, for instance, are of different appearance to those found in the south-east.

Windmill Sails

Old windmills had sails of basic design - simply cloths attached to wooden frames. The amount of sail area was varied manually by the miller according to the amount of wind and the work required. Manually-adjusted sails required the miller to interrupt his tasks in the mill to adjust the sails. Also, the mill needed a reliable brake to stop the sails. This led to the invention of automatic sails, where the effective area was varied by means of shutters. Early designs of automatic sails used spring pressure to control sail area according to the power demands of the milling process and varying wind conditions. However, these still required the mill to be stopped for every individual sail adjustment; but at least the mill was less likely to run away in strong winds. This all led to the invention of the automatic, or patent sail, where the effective area could be controlled by adjusting weights hanging from a chain suspended from the rear of the mill. The more power required, the heavier the controlling weights hung on the chain. As the wind became stronger, the weight lifted and wind spilled through the sails.

For maximum power to be extracted, it was also necessary for the axis of the sails to point into the wind. On early mills this was done by means of a tailpole, a long lever attached to the movable cap of a tower mill, or to the body in the case of a post mill. The tailpole enabled the miller to push the mill or its cap around its axis until it pointed into the wind; wind direction was often indicated by a small vane, mounted high up at the rear of the mill. The problem with this further manual adjustment was that it also interrupted work inside the mill and the serving of customers. This led to the invention of automatic systems for winding windmills, or keeping them pointing into the wind. This was achieved by mounting a small wind wheel at right angles to the airflow high up and or to the rear of the mill. This detected when the mill was coming out of the wind; it started rotating, and drove the mill back into the wind by a system of spindles and gears, which were attached either to a gear ring around the top of the tower, or to wheels running on the ground, attached to steps at the rear of a post mill.

Millstones

Most wind and watermills were constructed for grinding cereal grains for flour or animal feed using horizontally-mounted millstones. The milling machinery is very similar between wind and watermills and across geographic regions. Slight variations in the milling process occur in upland and northern regions; here, the main cereal milled may be not be wheat, but oats or rye. (Wheat does not ripen reliably in upland regions above one thousand feet in altitude). Most country mills also produced animal feedstuffs, but this trade was not so profitable as the production of high-quality flour for human consumption. This situation remains true today. Also, high-quality grain of suitable milling varieties is necessary for the production of white flour.

Steam Power

The invention of the steam engine, together with the design of safer boilers which burned cheap coal, led to the use of steam power for a variety of purposes. Steam power started to be used as an assisting power source for water and wind mills from about 1800 onwards. Before long, large mills were being designed and constructed which used steam as a sole power source. Furthermore, these mills were located near towns and ports where transport was available, and near to large numbers of customers. Ocean-going steam ships increased the availability of imported grain, which was of superior quality for flour milling and cheaper than home-produced varieties. So the location of large steam-powered mills near to ports was commercially attractive. Steam railways provided a means for distributing bulk

grain supplies to mills, and coal supplies for steam engines. Coastal shipping was also used to transport coal and grain within Britain. This large-scale commercial development using steam power led to a rapid decline of country milling in Britain. By 1900, large modern steam-powered mills had taken most of the flour trade away from country mills. The use of steam power to generate electricity for public supply rapidly increased from 1930 onwards. This led to the use of electric motors as a clean and efficient means of powering mill machinery, and also of safely lighting mill interiors.

Roller Mills

Roller mills use steel rolls rotating at slightly different speeds to reduce grain to flour. The process was invented in Europe in the 1850s, and rapidly spread to Britain. Roller mills are more efficient at producing flour than millstones, and it is easier to control quality. They are easily powered by steam engines or electric motors, and their widespread use was a reason for the rapid decline of country milling after 1900. Some traditional wind and watermills installed small roller mills to try to keep up with new technology, but they were no match for large installations located in towns and ports. Roller mills are almost exclusively used for large-scale cereal milling in modern times.

Modern Times

Most traditional wind and water mills were disused by 1940. A few have survived in working order, mainly owing to enthusiastic owners and millers. A very few have been in continuous trade, but most survive as novelty examples of past technology. Some are still viable businesses, supplying high quality stone-ground flour to a small specialist discerning market. As wind and watermills became appreciated as landscape features, so schemes to conserve representative examples became more common. Other uses for redundant mill buildings have been found: these mainly involve conversion to other uses, often housing, or sometimes business accommodation. High-technology wind generators are now being used to generate electricity, and are located in remote windy parts of Britain. Small-scale waterpower installations are used to provide electric power; these are usually in remote places which have more than adequate water flows in rivers and streams.

The Future

In the third millennium, about half of the mills illustrated in this book survive in one form or another. A third of the mills are accessible to visitors or customers. Some are working museums; others have been converted to tourist accommodation, and some to restaurants. Readers who feel that they would like to sample the atmosphere and experience of British traditional country mills have access to many fine examples located on impressive sites spread throughout Britain. Visitors will also meet the present day millers who have lots of enthusiasm to continue the milling trade. For more information on mills open to view, see 'Mills Open', published by the Mills Section of the Society for the Protection of Ancient Buildings, 37 Spital Square, London EC1 6DY. Another large owner is the National Trust (NT). Please consult local and regional offices of the NT for further information about visiting their properties. See national telephone directories for local information. For mills which have been converted to holiday accommodation, restaurants, theatres and shops, the easiest way to have a closer look is to become a customer.

East Midlands & East Anglia

*Burgh Le Marsh
The Windmill c1955 BS13022*

Aldeburgh, The Mill House 1909 62012
This is Fort Green Mill. It has a brick tower which once had four patent sails and a fantail. It was converted to a private house in 1902. The scene is now little different from that shown in the photograph.

◄ **Boston**
The Windmill c1965
B155096
This tall Lincolnshire-style brick tower mill, seven storeys high, was built in 1819; it was powered by five patent sails and winded by a fantail. The photograph shows the mill in a disused state and with no shutters in the sails before it was bought for preservation. It has now been restored to full working order, and is used for commercial milling. A Grade I listed building, it is privately owned and open to visitors.

◄ **Biggleswade
The Mills 1925** 77219
We are on the River Ivel, a tributary of the Great Ouse. This is a large brick-built mill alongside a navigable river; it is now converted into flats.

Burgh Le Marsh ►
The Windmill c1955
B513022
This typical Lincolnshire brick tower mill is powered by five patent shuttered sails and winded by a fantail. It was built in 1813, and worked by wind until 1964. It is preserved complete, and open to visitors; a building in the mill yard is now converted into a restaurant.

◄ **Bourn
The Mill c1955** B713009
This small historic black-tarred weatherboarded post mill with an open trestle is powered by two common and two spring sails, and is turned to the wind manually by a tail pole. Dated 1636, it ceased work in 1925. Owned by the Cambridge Preservation Society, it is preserved complete, and is open to visitors.

Burwell, The Mill c1955 B728009K

Here we see a Cambridgeshire brick tower mill photographed in the year when it ceased regular work. The four-storey tower is built of clunch, a hard chalk, which is protected from the weather by plastering. It has four patent shuttered sails and a fantail. It was built around 1820, and worked until 1955. It has been restored complete, and is open to visitors; a country village museum is located adjacent to the mill site.

Carlton in Lindrick, The Mill House c1965 C491014

The mill, on a tributary of the River Ryton, is a local sandstone building with an archway which forms a porch to the front entrance. The stonework is attributed to a Charles Battersby, who also designed the nearby bridge in 1717. The mill is powered by an internal breastshot waterwheel. It is privately owned and under restoration; some machinery is retained.

Horstead, The Mill 1902 48149

Horstead Mill on the River Bure navigation, a fine white weatherboarded flour mill with a multi-valley roof, is pictured while it was in full working order. It was powered by a breast shot waterwheel at one end and a turbine at the other. The mill was equipped for loading mill materials to and from boats by means of two lucams and a small crane. The wherry 'Widgeon' is delivering a cargo of timber. Alas, the mill was burnt down in 1963. The site is now landscaped foundations.

▼ **Coningsby, The Mill c1955** C429003
The mill was a Lincolnshire-style brick tower with an onion-shaped cap. It had five patent shuttered sails, as is indicated by the five-way cross on the front of the windshaft, and a fantail. It was built in 1826, and the remains were demolished in 1970.

▼ **Downham Market, Denver Mill c1965** D211003
Denver Mill is a tall brick tower mill with four patent shuttered sails and a fantail. The brickwork is rendered all over to assist with weather protection. The mill is shown in the photograph at a time when it was still trading, but not using windpower. Built in 1835, it ceased work by wind in 1941. Now restored complete, and demonstrated in working order, it is open to visitors.

▲ **Edlesborough
The Ford and the Mill
c1965** E165008
Here we see the brick tower mill, with a replacement roof in place of a cap, in a stripped-down and derelict condition. The photograph was taken from a nearby watermill site. Windmills and watermills were often sited near to each other; the two very different power sources complemented one another where there was a total dependence on natural power sources. The windmill is now converted to a private house.

◀ **Flatford**
Flatford Mill 1907 57551
We are on the River Stour. The scene still looks largely the same as it did when it was painted by the landscape artist John Constable in 1817; his father was a miller. The mill is now conserved externally, but is empty of machinery. The mill is owned by the National Trust and leased to the Field Studies Council, who run arts-based courses for all age groups; it is only open to students and pre-arranged tour groups.

Fulbourn ▶
The Old Mill c1950
F104001

This is a fine old Cambridgeshire smock mill with four patent shuttered sails and a fantail; it was built in 1808, and ceased work in 1937. The photograph shows the mill when it was disused and before restoration work began. Privately owned, and restored in complete but non-working condition, it is open to visitors two days a year, or by appointment.

▼ Godmanchester, The Old Mill 1898 41273

This old weatherboarded mill on the River Great Ouse navigation is in derelict condition. The timber framing has become weakened, and the whole structure is leaning badly. A large low breastshot waterwheel was housed in the semi-circular shelter in front of the mill. The view in the photograph is from the headrace side of the mill, and shows the debris guard in the water intake - the spectators are standing above it on the bridge; waterborne debris flowing down a river was a big problem, and it had to be prevented from entering, and damaging, waterwheels. The mill is now completely gone.

▲ Grantchester
The Old Mill 1914
66908A

We are at the upper limit of the River Cam navigation. This is a large brick-built mill with a mansarded tiled roof. An old-style pleasure boat is shown in the foreground. A popular mode of leisure travel from the city is by punt, and a nearby tea-garden is a relaxing place to obtain refreshments. The mill was burnt down in 1928, and a house has been built on the site.

◄ **Grantham**
The Mill c1960 G43071
This water mill, in flat country on the River Witham some distance from the sea, is viewed from the headrace water channel. The brick building has a slate roof and a sack hoist lantern. Modern, hand wheel-operated, guillotine-type sluices control the water flow. The mill is now converted into a house.

Haddenham, The Mill c1950 H249007

Great Mill is a yellow brick tower windmill standing on a ridge, with panoramic views of the flat fenland. The tower is four storeys high, and its diameter is larger than normal, particularly at the top. The mill has four patent sails and is winded by a fantail. It was built in 1803 and ceased work in 1943. It has now been restored, and is complete with all its original machinery. It is privately owned, but is sometimes open to visitors.

Hinxton, The Mill and the River c1960 H441007

We are on the River Cam. The building is of wooden weatherboarded construction with a tiled roof. The mill was originally powered by a breast shot waterwheel, which was removed in 1913 and replaced by a Canadian-made 'Little Giant' turbine. A corn mill, it was used in the past as a vegetable oil mill (vegetable oils were used for smokeless lighting); the miller also sold beer. Privately owned, it is restored and open to visitors, and is demonstrated in working order.

Heckington, The Mill c1955 H63015
This is a brick tower mill with eight patent shuttered sails and a fantail. The massive sail arrangement is now unique in a traditional type of windmill - windmills having more than four sails were never numerous. It was built in 1803 and ceased work in 1942; it has been restored to working order, and is open to visitors.

**Hornchurch
The Mill 1909** 62085
This is an East Anglian-style post mill with a white-painted weatherboarded body, four spring patent shuttered sails and winded manually by a tailpole.
The photograph shows the mill in full working order, but idle; the mill door is closed, with the security bar in place. A man and a two-wheeled horse and cart and the boys in the foreground wait patiently for the photographer to complete his record. The mill ceased work in 1912, and was accidentally burnt down in 1921.

◄ **Houghton**
The Mill 1899 44257
This large black
weatherboarded mill on the
River Great Ouse navigation
is pictured in working order
when it was still trading.
Power was provided by
three large breast shot
waterwheels. It ceased work
in 1930, and was used as a
Youth Hostel for forty years.
Owned by the National Trust,
it has now been restored as
a mill and partly returned
to working order; open to
visitors, it is demonstrated
with one new waterwheel
and millstones.

Horsey
The Windmill c1955
H341018

Here we see a typical Broadland brick tower drainage mill. It has four patent sails and a fantail, and drove a turbine pump. Owned by the National Trust, it is conserved in complete but non-working condition, and is open to visitors.

Madingley
The Ruined Windmill
1909 61524

Here we see an old post windmill in its last stages of decay. It appears that the mill has been used as a source of firewood. Note the remains of the primitive common sails, and also the two old-style poultry coops in the foreground. A replacement post mill was moved to the site in 1936; it still exists, but is not open to visitors.

Kibworth Harcourt
The Old Mill c1955
K119033

This is a midland-type post mill with the body stabilised by the round-house roof structure. It was fitted with two common cloth spread and two spring sails, and was winded manually by means of a tailpole. Dated 1711, it ceased work in 1916. Conserved and owned by the Society for the Protection of Ancient Buildings, it is open to visitors by appointment only.

◄ **Mundesley**
Paston Stow Mill c1960
M109084
This is a brick tower mill with four patent sails and winded by a fantail. The sail frames are empty, the shutters are removed. Also note the staging around the cap, but not on the tower; the sails were low enough to work on them from ground level. The mill was built in 1827 and last worked by wind in 1930. The mill is conserved, but is internally incomplete; it is privately owned and open to visitors.

◀ **Market Rasen
The Mill c1955** M231021
This tall brick building on the River Rasen, which flows into the River Ancholme, was originally built as a canal warehouse. When the canal scheme failed, the building was converted to a corn mill powered by a waterwheel, which was later replaced by a turbine.

Over, The Mill c1965 ▶
O114010
A brick tower mill, this was photographed at about the time it was purchased by a mill enthusiast for preservation. The brick tower is tarred black for extra weather protection. It has four patent shuttered sails, and is winded by a fantail. The mill was built in about 1860. It has now been restored to full working order, and is regularly worked to produce wholemeal flour. It is privately owned, and open to visitors by appointment.

Pakenham ▶
The Windmill c1955
P286003
This is a typical Suffolk brick tower mill with four patent shuttered sails and a fantail. The mill was used as the subject of a TV interlude film in 1950s, and was watched by millions of viewers. It has been owned by the same family since the 1880s; conserved in working order, it is privately owned and open to visitors by appointment.

◀ **Sandy**
The Mill 1925 77228
This brick building with a slate roof and a two-storey waterwheel house stands on the River Ivel, which flows into the Great Ouse and thence to the Wash. The river has ideal conditions for waterfowl, who probably benefited from spilt grain and mill waste. Note the sandbagged riverbank. The mill has now gone - it was demolished in 1977.

Horning
The Mill 1902 48110

A small hollow post wind pump for land drainage, the mill had shuttered sails and was turned to the wind by twin tail vanes. The shutters in the sails were set manually, one sail at a time. The mill would have been stopped by turning it out of the wind by pulling on a rope attached to the tail vanes. These small low-cost windpumps were quite widely used in the Broads area; similar mills are preserved at Upton and How Hill, and can be visited.

Soham
The Mill c1955 S597006

Here we see Lion Mills at Soham Lode on the River Snail, a modernised mill located in Fenland. The mill was originally powered by a breast shot waterwheel supplemented by a steam engine. A water turbine was installed in about 1900, and is used to drive an electric generator. This is remarkable, considering the flatness of the surrounding countryside and the distance from the sea. The original mill was built in 1811, but it was rebuilt in 1948 after a fire. It is a working commercial mill business.

South Normanton
The Old Windmill c1955

S725012

Here we see a post mill with an open trestle in its last stage of dereliction. The picture clearly shows the structural framing of a post mill with its trestle. It is remarkable in that it shows a complete lack of diagonal bracing to stiffen the structure: a lot of the stresses caused to the structure when the mill was working would have been passed to the weatherboarding, not a very good idea. The mill was built around 1805; it ceased working in 1908, and was dismantled in 1980.

South Ockendon, The Windmill c1960 S280022
This is actually a combined wind and water mill. A smockmill with a weatherboarded tower, boat shaped cap and octagonal brick base, and powered by four patent shuttered sails and winded by a fantail, it was built beside a millpond; a waterwheel was added at the side of the base, which drove an additional pair of millstones. Auxiliary steam power was also provided from an outbuilding. Built in about 1829, it ceased working in 1923 and collapsed in 1977.

South Wigston, Crow Mill c1960 S548008
Standing on the River Sence, which flows into the River Soar, a tributary of the River Trent, this brick building with a slate roof is stripped of all machinery. The empty waterwheel space can be seen under the arch. The large roof ventilator is evidence of a drying kiln or machine.

Stafford, Children's Park and the Old Mill c1955 S411017
Broad Eye Mill was originally a seven-storey tower mill built of sandstone blocks on the site of a pre-Norman castle; it is sometimes referred to as Castle Hill Mill. Built in 1796, it ceased work around 1900. It has been reduced in height, and is now being turned into an industrial heritage museum; it can be visited by appointment.

Sutton on Trent, The Mill and the Mill House 1909 61824

Sutton on Trent
The Mill and the Mill House 1909
This is a typical Nottinghamshire brick tower mill, tall and black-tarred. The photograph shows the mill in full working order. It was built in 1825, and ceased work by wind in about 1930 and by engine in 1940; the cap was removed in 1934. It was painted by the artist Karl Wood in 1931 in a derelict condition; it is now converted to a private house.

Sutton
The Windmill c1955
This is a very tall brick tower mill with a boat shaped cap, four patent shuttered sails and a fantail. Built in 1789, it ceased work after lightning damage in 1940. This is one of the tallest tower windmills in Britain, nine stories high, with a staging on a level with the sixth floor. Now being restored, it is privately owned and open to visitors.

Sutton, The Windmill c1955 S473016

Thorpeness
The House in the Clouds and the Mill c1955 T38012
This post mill was moved to here from Aldringham in 1922, and
was altered to drive a waterpump to provide water supplies for a
holiday village. The house in the clouds conceals a water storage
tank. It is now conserved and open to visitors.

**The Broads
The Mill and the
River c1934** T213064
A quiet scene showing
a drainage tower mill
starting to fall into
disrepair; two blades of
the fantail are missing.
The patent sails appear
to be empty of shutters.
By this time, land
drainage had mainly
been entrusted to
engine and electrically-
driven pumps,
rendering windmill
pumps obsolete
and only kept as a
landscape feature.

Thetford, Mill Head 1929 81834
We are on the River Wissey, which flows into the River Great Ouse, at the head of the navigable river; there were cost advantages in milling in such locations, particularly in areas where the roads were bad, thus causing local transport difficulties.

Turvey, The Mill c1955 T90021
This large brick and timber building is set on the River Great Ouse. The Statue on the island in the foreground is of Jonah. The mill is now converted to housing.

Upminster, The Mill 1908 59867
A fine white weatherboarded smock mill, it stands on a single-storey brick base with a stage at first-floor level and also around the cap. The photograph shows the mill in full working order, powered by four patent shuttered sails and winded by a fantail. Dated 1803, it ceased regular work in about 1930; it is now conserved complete and open to visitors.

Willingham
The Mill c1955 W510001

Cattell's Mill is a black-tarred weatherboarded smock windmill on an octagonal single-storey brick base. The photograph shows the mill in the last years of its working life; it is reduced to two sails. Built in 1828, it ceased working by wind in about 1962. Privately owned, it is now restored complete and is sometimes open to visitors.

Wisbech
The Mill 1929 81981

This is a tall brick tower mill with a large extension grafted onto it to house a steam-driven mill. It had eight sails, as we can see from the eight-armed cross on the windshaft. Note the tall brick chimney above the roofline for the steam boiler. The shell of the mill tower has now been slightly reduced in height and converted into a private house.

Willingham, The Mill c1955 W510001

Wisbech, The Mill 1929 81981

The West Midlands & Central England

Abingdon
Abbey Mill 1890 26992
Abbey Mill is on the River Thames navigation, built on an old abbey mill site, which has been redeveloped over the years. It is of stone and part weatherboarded construction with a tiled roof. It is now converted to a hotel; its waterwheel is retained in situ.

▼ **Bibury, Arlington Mill c1955** B530025
A stone building with stone roof, Arlington Mill is on the River Colne; it was worked as a corn and fulling mill until 1907. The milling machinery was scrapped in 1914, but it has now been replaced by similar gearing taken from a nearby mill. It is now reconstructed as a mill museum at the Cotswold country museum, and is open to visitors; it is powered by an electric motor, as there is no waterwheel.

▼ **Bidford-on-Avon, Cleeve Mill 1901** 47335
Cleeve Mill, on the River Avon, which flows into the River Severn, is a stone building with tiled roof. A man-made weir impounds the river flow and directs it towards the mill. The boaters are rowing towards more lively water. The mill appears to be in poor repair; the roof is not in a good state, which may indicate that the mill is already disused. The mill has been gone for many years now, and only overgrown foundations remain.

▲ **Bramshott
The Flour Mill 1901**
46587
The mill building of brick and stone with a half-hipped tiled roof is on the River Wey. The mill has now gone, demolished many years ago.

◀ **Bromfield**
The Mill and the Church
1892 30842

The saw mill stands on the bank of the River Teme. It is part of the Oakly Park estate, home of the Earl of Plymouth. The waterwheel is prominent in the foreground, and is protected by a roof. The mill was later converted to turbine drive. It still exists, but has been disused for many years.

**Mapledurham
The Mill 1890** 27091
This brick and timber building with a tiled roof on the River Thames has a prominent sack hoist lantern projecting above the roofline. As we can see, two low breastshot waterwheels power the mill. A turbine later replaced the left-hand waterwheel. A horse-drawn water cart, in the foreground, is being filled from the river; it is interesting to consider for what purpose the river water was being collected. The mill, which is open to visitors, is now restored to working order using one waterwheel, and regularly produces flour.

◄ **Pangbourne
The Mill 1910** 62225
The mill was built on the
River Pang, a tributary of
the River Thames. The
mill has now gone, and
its site is incorporated
into a waterworks.

◀ **Ironbridge**
The Waterwheel 1892 30898
Benthall corn mill, on the River Severn, was an old mill with a sixty-foot diameter backshot waterwheel taking advantage of a high head of water. Sited near to the Iron Bridge, this mill was painted by the artist Paul Sandby Munn in 1802; the original painting is in the possession of the Ironbridge Gorge Museum Trust. This photograph shows the waterwheel in working order; now, only ruins of the building survive.

▼ **Shiplake**
The Mill and the Lock 1890 27167
A fine range of buildings is spread out along the bank of the River Thames. A tall brick chimney indicates the use of steam power. This was a corn mill, which was later converted to papermaking. The mill was demolished in 1907.

◀ **Sonning**
The Mill c1955 S149036
The large white weatherboarded flourmill stands on an island in the River Thames. It was a roller-type mill, powered by two low breastshot water wheels and an oil engine. The photograph shows only part of the mill. It ceased working as a mill in 1969, and is now converted to a theatre and restaurant.

Streatley, The Mill and the Bridge 1890 27043
This was a large riverside mill on the River Thames. Now only the mill site and the sluices exist.

Sulhamstead, Tyle Mill c1955 T254007
We are on the River Kennet, which flows into the Thames. This was a large weatherboarded mill with flows from several water channels passing under the mill; it has now gone. The mill has been demolished and a house built on the foundations.

The North

Acomb
The Old Mill c1955 A250002
This range of stone buildings, dated 1728, stands in a rural location
on the Birkey Burn, which flows into the Tyne. It is powered by an
overshot waterwheel, and it also had a steam engine; it is privately
owned. A windmill tower is nearby.

Hawes, The Mill 1900 45641
The mill is in Wensleydale, and stands on the Duerley Beck, which flows into the River Ure. A stone building with a slate roof, it is a corn mill powered by an overshot waterwheel. It would seem likely that the waterwheel has been stopped for the photograph to be taken, because water is gushing from the by-pass sluice and spectators are watching from the bridge. The mill building is now empty of all machinery.

Barnard Castle, Demesnes Mill 1914 67182

We are on the River Tees. The stone building with a slate roof is located on the riverbank beside a natural rock weir. The height of the stone wall alongside the road, and the height of the mill sluices, show that the river is not always this placid, and that precautions have been taken against torrential floodwater. The mill, privately owned, still contains a waterwheel and some machinery.

Newcastle upon Tyne, The Old Mill c1887 16979

A stone building with a tiled roof, the mill is in Jesmond Dene on the River Ouseburn, a tributary of the Tyne. Powered by an overshot waterwheel, the mill was used as a corn mill, and was later adapted to grind flint for a pottery. This was a much-photographed mill in Victorian and Edwardian times. It is now conserved in a public park with a replacement waterwheel.

◄ **Loftus**
Loftus Mill c1955
L159018
Loftus Mill, a stone building with tiled roof, stands on a tributary of Kilton Beck. The attached house is a later addition: note the join line in the stonework and the small step in the roofline. The mill has two domestic-style chimney stacks, probably for fireplaces to provide a bit of warmth for the miller during a long winter. The neatly-kept vegetable garden is noteworthy.

Kirkby-in-Furness
The Mill c1960
K114021
The mill stands on Gill House Beck; it is a stone building with slate roof, and was powered by an overshot waterwheel. We can see that it has been converted into a house, complete with modern window frames.

Sedbergh
Forsters Mill 1891
28336
We are on the River Lune, which flows into Morecambe Bay. This stone-built mill is in poor condition: the waterwheel appears to have gone, and the mill looks abandoned.

Tadcaster
The Mill 1906 54852
This large brick-built mill has an equally large chimney and engine house, which indicates the use of steam power. The mill, which was on the River Wharfe, has now gone.

◀ **Alderley Edge
The Old Mill 1896** 37478
This is a red sandstone building
with a long sloping stone catslide
roof close to the dam of a lake at
the rear of the mill. It is powered
by two overshot waterwheels,
which are unusually arranged in
tandem, one above the other.
The wooden building in front
of the mill housed an auxiliary
engine. The building to the right
of the mill was a grain drying kiln
and store, and this part has now
gone. The mill worked until 1939.
Owned by the National Trust, it is
conserved complete; it is open to
visitors, and is demonstrated in
working order.

◀ Whitby
Rigg Mill 1885 18177

Rigg Mill, on Rigg Mill Beck which flows into the River Esk, is a stone building with a very large diameter breastshot waterwheel mounted at the end wall of the mill, with drive to the mill machinery via a cog ring gear. The wooden rim and arms of the wheel are decaying, showing that the mill is no longer being worked by water power. The long narrow table and hard bench seating seem to await people enjoying the view whilst taking refreshments. A besom broom is to hand ready to sweep the cobbled yard.

▼ Bowdon
Dunham Mill 1892 30392

This saw mill on Dunham Massey Park estate is a brick building with stone dressings and a slate roof. It is powered by an overshot waterwheel which drives a large frame saw, a circular saw and a bandsaw via flat belting. It was originally a corn mill, which was then refitted as a sawmill in about 1860. It was disused in 1895, so the picture shows the mill in the last years of its regular working life. Now restored to working order and open to visitors, it is owned by the National Trust.

◀ Crosby
The Windmill c1960
C357017

Great Crosby Mill, Liverpool is a tall brick tower mill with a domed cap. It had four common cloth sails and a fantail. Dated 1813, it had ceased work by 1900; it is now converted into to a private house.

Lytham, From the Pier 1894 33958
The brick tower windmill with four patent sails and a fantail stands on the Green, overlooking the River Ribble estuary. The main leisure activity shown in the photograph is donkey and horse rides on the beach. The sea defences look to be in good repair, and the Green area is remarkably clear of wheeled transport. The mill was built in 1805 and ceased working in 1919; it is now conserved and open to visitors.

Thornton Cleveleys, Marsh Mill c1955 T307001
Marsh Windmill is a large Fylde-type brick tower mill with four patent shuttered sails and a fantail. Dated 1794, it worked until 1922. The picture shows the mill in a disused condition before restoration work began. It is now conserved complete, and is open to visitors as part of a craft workshops site.

The South-East

Alderholt
The Mill c1960 A310007
Alderholt Mill stands on the Allen River, a
brick building with a slate roof. It is powered
by a breastshot waterwheel, which drives two
pairs of millstones. It is open to visitors, and is
demonstrated in working order.

The Broads, The Mill and the River c1934 T213064

◄ **Andover**
Rooksbury Mill 1906
54632
The mill is a brick and
weatherboard building
with tiled roofing. It is
now used as a fish farm.
It stands on a tributary
of the River Test.

◀ **Andover**
Anton Mill 1906
54631
A large brick building with a tiled roof, the mill stands on the River Anton, a tributary of the River Test. It is now used as a workshop.

Willesborough ▶
The Windmill 1909 61562
Here we see a fine example of a white weatherboarded Kentish smock mill with a two-storey square brick base and wooden staging for access to the sails. It is powered by four patent shuttered sails and winded by a fantail. Dated 1869, it worked to 1938. It is now restored to full working order and is open to visitors.

▲ **Bembridge**
The Old Windmill
c1955 B64301
This is a stone tower windmill with four common, cloth spread sails. It was winded by hand by means of an endless chain which hung from a chainwheel at the rear of the cap down to the ground. The mill ceased work 1913, and is now restored to complete, but non-working condition; it is open to visitors and owned by the National Trust.

Biddenden
The Windmill c1955
B88001
This is a Kentish white weatherboarded smock mill with a two-storey octagonal brick base, powered by four patent shuttered sails and winded by a fantail. It has now gone, and the site is built over.

Bentley
Isington Mill c1955
168002

Isington Mill stands on the River Wey, a brick building with a tiled roof with two undershot waterwheels. It was converted to a private house in 1947; it was the retirement home of the late Field Marshall Lord Montgomery of Alamein.

Bordon
Headley Mill Lake
c1960 B143032

By the River Wey, a large millpond feeds a breast shot waterwheel driving four pairs of millstones producing flour and animal feed. A small lorry awaits trade. The mill is still worked commercially by members of a family who have owned the mill since 1914; it is open to visitors by appointment.

Bosham
The Old Mill 1903
50921

The old black weatherboarded mill stands on Bosham Stream by the shore of Chichester Harbour; it had three overshot waterwheels. A hoist lantern is visible at the roofline between the two parts of the mill building. The mill has now been reconstructed, and is used as a yacht club.

▼ **Botley, The Mills c1950** B544006

The large watermill, dating from 1770, is sited on the navigable River Hamble. It was modernised by adding grain silos, a roller mill and a water turbine, which powers millstones. The mill is now restored as a museum of flour milling, with craft shops and restaurant. The mill can be visited by appointment.

▼ **Bramley, The Mill 1935** 87042

Bramley Mill, on the River Wey, was a busy mill owing to its extensive mill pond, which gave a reliable water supply. The mill ceased working in 1931; the machinery was removed in 1935, and the mill was converted to a private house.

▲ **Carisbrooke The Castle and the Old Mill c1955** C26035

The photograph shows the mill in the corner of a range of buildings. Lukely Brook feeds the millpond. The brick mill building has a tiled roof. The mill was powered by an overshot waterwheel; it has now collapsed.

◄ **Chartham**
The Mill on the River
Stour 1903 50361
This was a large corn mill
located on the river bank.
It has now been converted
into a private house.

Churt, Barford Mill 1906 55517
This corn mill, standing on a tributary to the River Wey, is a wooden weatherboarded building on a brickwork base with a half-hipped tiled roof. A millpond supplies an overshot waterwheel. The miller is looking out of a hatch above the waterwheel sluice with a shovel under his arm. The leaning side of the mill is propped by a wooden pole resting in the millpond. The mill was worked up to 1914, but it has since been demolished and replaced by a private house.

Cobham, The Mill 1919 68857
A pair of similar mills with brick buildings and tiled roofing stand on the River Mole. They were powered by breastshot waterwheels. They ceased work in 1928, and in 1953 one mill was demolished to make room for a road widening scheme. The remaining mill has now been restored to working order; open to visitors, it provides milling demonstrations.

Cranbrook, Union Mill 1906 56972
Union Mill is a white weatherboarded Kentish-style smock mill on a three-storey octagonal brick base with a
staging. It has four patent shuttered sails and a fantail. It is the tallest smock mill in Britain, measuring 72 feet
from ground level to the ridge of the cap. It was built in 1814, and ceased trading in 1950. The mill has now been
restored to full working order and is open to visitors.

◄ **Dorking, Pixham Mill
1931** 84182
Pixham Mill stands
on the Pippbrook,
which flows into the
River Mole. It is a
brick building with a
slated roof, and was
powered by an overshot
waterwheel. Rebuilt in
1837, it had ceased
work by 1930, and is
now converted into a
private house.

Dorking, Castle Mill c1960 D45103

Named after Betchworth castle, the mill stands on the River Mole. The building is of brick and white weatherboard with a mansarded slated roof. It was powered by a breastshot waterwheel. The mill ceased work in 1952, and is now converted into a private house.

Elstead The Mill 1906 55626

The tall brick building with a half-hipped tiled roof topped by a cupola stands on the River Wey. Its past use was as a textile and a corn mill, powered by a large undershot waterwheel. It ceased work 1878, so it had already finished work as a mill when this photo was taken. It is now converted to a restaurant, with the waterwheel visible through a glass window.

Emsworth The Old Mill c1955 E62031

This is Quay Tide Mill, set on Emsworth Channel, which leads to the English Channel. It is a timber-framed building with brick infill and a tiled roof. It had an undershot waterwheel, but it has not worked by tide since 1921; the machinery is now removed, and it is privately owned.

◀ **Farnham**
Moor Park Mill 1913
65936
High Mill, on the River
Wey, is built of brick
and weatherboard
with a tiled half-hipped
roof. Powered by an
undershot waterwheel,
it worked until 1950; it
is now used for storage
and is privately owned.

Ewhurst
The Mill 1925 78108
Hurt Wood Mill is a small brick tower mill with four patent sails and a fantail. It is located on a remote hilltop surrounded by woodland. The mill has now been converted into a private house.

Fittleworth
The Mill 1908 60184
The mill stands on the River Rother, and is built of local stone with brick quoins and dressings. It had two undershot waterwheels. The mill was derelict by 1937, and it is now converted to a private house.

Frimley Green
The Old Windmill 1906 54908
This red brick tower mill was built in 1784 and was disused by 1870. It was converted into a house in 1914, and now forms part of a large private country house.

**Gomshall
The Mill 1904** 51810
Gomshall Mill stands on
the River Tillingbourne.
It is of brick and
timber construction
with tiled roofing. It
was powered by two
overshot waterwheels,
which were housed
within the building;
one waterwheel
was removed and
scrapped in 1939. The
photograph shows
the mill when it was in
full working order and
trading as a country
mill; the girls are
paddling in the tailrace.
The mill continued
working until 1953.
This fine old watermill is
conserved, and used as
an antiques gallery
and restaurant.

Godalming, The Flour Mill 1908 59952

Hatch Mill lies beside a tributary to the River Wey. It is a brick and timber building with a tiled roof with dormer windows and a hoist lantern. The low floor level of the weatherboarded extension to the water level in the pond is notable. A large brick boiler chimney is evidence of steam power. A water turbine was installed in 1940 and is still in situ. The mill ceased work 1950, and is now used for private industrial use and storage.

Guildford ▶
Stoke Mill c1955
G65064

This large brick built mill is dated 1879; it was a modern turbine-powered roller flourmill. Now converted to offices, it stands on the River Wey.

▲ Goudhurst
Hope Mill 1901 46398

This brick and weatherboarded building with a half-hipped tiled roof stands on the River Teise. It was powered by one breastshot and one overshot waterwheel. The young passengers in the boat are all dressed in uniform. The mill is now converted to a private house with a waterwheel.

Godstone
Ivy Mill 1898 42753
The brick, stone and wooden mill building is on the Gibbs Brook. The mill worked until 1922, and was destroyed by fire in 1924. It has now gone - only the footings remain.

Havant, Langstone Mill c1955 L481311

Horndean, The Windmill c1965 H403047

Havant
Langstone Mill c1955
The brick windmill tower is an unusual shape. It is sited on the sea shore of Langstone Harbour, near the mill house and a converted watermill. The windmill now forms part of a private house.

Horndean
The Windmill c1965
Chalton Down Mill was a brick tower windmill located on a remote hill top overlooking the main London to Portsmouth road. It was powered by four patent shuttered sails and winded by a fantail. Built in 1785, it ceased work around 1885, and is now converted into a private house.

High Salvington, The Old Mill 1919 68994
This is a fine old Sussex downland post mill with a domesticated structure enclosing the trestle. Powered by two common cloth sails, the mill was turned into the wind by means of a tailpole. It was built in around 1710 and worked to 1894, and again until 1914. The photograph shows the mill with common sails, when the site was used as a tea garden. The mill is now restored to working order, with an original-style roundhouse enclosing the trestle, and is open to visitors.

Horsham, Town Mill 1891 29722
Town Mill, a large brick-built mill with a tiled roof, lies on the River Arun. It had an iron overshot waterwheel, together with an alternative breast shot wheel for use when the river was flooding. Four pairs of millstones were driven by waterpower, and an auxiliary beam-type steam-engine was also used. The photograph shows a quiet stretch of the river which formed the headrace to the mill. The mill worked until the 1950s; it has now been converted into a private house, with all the machinery removed.

Ickham, Seaton Mill 1903 49436
This black weatherboarded building, with a separate brick building and a chimney housing a steam engine, stands on the River Little Stour. It has now been converted to a private house.

Kennington, The Mill 1901 47543
Wind, water and steam mills are all sited together: here we see a Kentish-style smock mill, together with a large brick-built water mill and a steam mill. A tall brick boilerhouse chimney extends to nearly the height of the windmill cap. The smoke and fumes discharged from the chimney would have smoked up the windmill when it was downwind. The steam mill probably did most of the work, as it was the most reliable power source. The windmill was built in 1813; its tower was demolished in 1952, leaving just the roofed-over base.

**Leatherhead
The Old Mill 1906**

54882

This range of mainly timber buildings with tiled roofing stands on the Hogsmill River. It was a flourmill powered by a large breastshot waterwheel; then production changed to a linseed oil mill in 1878. The horse and cart seem to be waiting to ford the river as soon as the photographer has finished. The mill has now been demolished.

◄ **Meopham
The Green and the
Windmill c1965** M253048
This is a small Kentish-type smock mill with a six-sided black weatherboarded body and a hexagonal single-storey brick base with a staging. It is powered by four patent shuttered sails and winded by a fantail. The mill was built in about 1821, and ceased work by wind in 1927.
Now conserved complete, it is open to visitors.

Littlebourne
The Mill 1903 49432
Littlebourne Mill is a white weatherboarded building with a prominent brick chimney for a steam-engine boiler. Now converted to a private house, it stands on the River Little Stour.

Newark
The Mill 1903 49300
A very large white weatherboarded building with a tiled roof, the flour mill had two lucams, two sack hoist lanterns and loading ramps. The low level lucam was used for loading to boats on the River Wey. It was powered by three breastshot waterwheels. It ceased work in 1943, and was burnt down in 1963, alas.

Ockley
The Windmill 1906
55617
This is a smock windmill with some vertical weatherboarding and a single-storey brick base with staging. The mill was powered by four patent shuttered sails, and winding was controlled by hand with an endless chain gear hanging from the rear of the cap down to the staging. Only the brick base survives.

Outwood
The Windmills 1906
54733
This pair of windmills stand on Outwood Common: a post mill with two common and two spring sails and a roundhouse protecting the trestle, and also a tall weatherboarded smock mill. The smock mill collapsed in 1960. The post mill was built in 1665, and survives in full working order. There is an old story that the glow in the sky caused by the great fire of London was observed from the mill. Listed Grade I, it is privately owned and open to visitors.

Ramsgate, The Old Mill 1901 48045
Here we have a fine example of a black Kentish smock windmill in its heyday, and an early
photograph of a windmill in full working order. The mill has now completely gone.

Reigate, The Windmill 1893 33231 The mill stands on Wray Common, a brick tower mill with four patent sails winded by a fantail; it was built in 1824 and ceased work in about 1895. The scene shown in the photograph is still recognisable today. The mill has been converted into to a private house.

Reigate Heath, The Windmill c1965 R20214 The black-painted post mill with four patent sails is turned to the wind manually by a tailpole. Located near to a golf course, it was built in about 1765 and ceased work in about 1870. The roundhouse was converted into a chapel in 1880. The mill is owned by the Local Authority.

◄ **Romsey**
The Old Mill c1955
R53026
Saddler's Mill was built in 1748 on the River Test. It is a brick building with an attached house, both with tiled roofing; a turbine powered a pump. There is a salmon leap beside the mill. The photograph shows the headrace side of the mill. Privately owned, the mill is now used for storage; a fish farm also uses the site.

**▲ Rye
The Mill 1912**
64934
This was a white weatherboarded smock mill with a brick base. The photograph shows the mill in full working order. Alas, it was burnt down in 1932.

**▲ Rottingdean
From the Windmill
c1965** R62037
This black weatherboarded smock windmill stands in a striking position on the South Downs, overlooking the coastline. It is a picturesque and much-photographed mill which is now conserved as a landmark.

**Rye ▶
The Windmill
c1955** R77080
A dummy smock mill, this was built as an empty shell with no milling machinery. It was built to replace an earlier mill that was destroyed by fire. Now conserved, it forms part of a busy guesthouse.

▼ **Sherfield on Loddon, The Mill c1955** S631004
The mill is a partly brick and part timbered building with a tiled mansarded roof, standing on the River Loddon; it is powered by an internal breastshot waterwheel. Flour making ceased in 1895; the mill was worked from 1895 to 1977 by the same family. The mill was fire-damaged in 1991 and has now been reconstructed as a restaurant.

▼ **Stanwell Moor, The Old Mill c1955** S668008
Upper Mill stands on the River Colne; the building is of brick, with a slate roof and lucam, and the mill was powered by a breastshot waterwheel. Its past use was as a cornmill, a papermill and a dyeworks; it is now converted to other industrial use.

▲ **Westcott
The Rookery Mill
House 1933** 85494
Lower Mill is a small building of brick and timber, standing on the Pippbrook, a tributary of the River Mole. It was reconstructed as a house in 1945.

◀ **Wonersh
Lower Mill 1906** 55129
The mill building, of brick
and white weatherboard
construction with a tiled
roof, stands on a tributary
of the River Wey. The large
mill pond fed a turbine
which powered the mill.
The door behind the horse
loaded into the stone
floor, and the one above
to the grain bin floor. The
mill ceased working in
1910; the machinery is still
complete, and the mill is
now used for storage.
It is in private ownership.

Westwell, The Mill c1960 W404010
This mill is a brick and weatherboarded building with a tiled half-hipped roof; it was powered by an overshot
waterwheel. Now converted to a private house, it stands on a tributary of the River Great Stour.

The South-West

Allerford
Piles Mill 1931 84856

Piles Mill stands on the River Aller and is part of the Holnicote
Estate in Exmoor. A small stone building with a tiled roof, the
mill is powered by an overshot waterwheel. In the photograph
the waterwheel is stationary, with the by-pass sluice open; it
was probably stopped for the photograph to be taken. The long-
exposure photograph gives the impression of a torrent of water.
The mill had three pairs of millstones, of which two remain in situ;
it also crushed apples for cider production. It is preserved and
open to visitors, and owned by the National Trust.

▼ Boscastle, The Old Mill c1960 B149138

Set on the River Valency, this is a very fine example of a Cornish mill with an overshot waterwheel; the wheel turns for visual effect only, as no machinery remains in situ. The tailrace discharges to the harbour. The building, of local stone with a slate roof, is now converted to a shop, and is open to customers.

▼ Bude, Coombe Valley Mill 1929 82898

A small stream feeds an overshot waterwheel, and the tailrace discharges to the rocky Atlantic coast at Duckpool, where there is a small beach. The mill is a stone building with a slate roof and a small chimney. The auxiliary drive iron pulley wheel, near the corner of the mill, has been used for belt-driving a circular saw bench to cut logs for firewood. The mill is conserved complete; the area is now a holiday park owned by the National Trust, with lettings by the Landmark Trust.

▲ Bude
Millook 1920 69543

A small country mill with an overshot waterwheel is set in an isolated location very near to the sea at Millook Haven. The mill is mentioned in Parnall's 'Wreckers and Wrestlers', and it still exists. The mill house is now a holiday let.

◄ **Camelford**
The Mill and the Stream 1894 33587
The mill, a stone building with a slate roof, is on the River Camel. An overshot waterwheel is located on the corner of the building, with its water supply pentrough coming from between the buildings and turning sharply towards the top of the wheel. This is not a common arrangement; water supply channels are usually kept as straight as possible for best water flow. The rocky tailrace stream in the foreground is dry, but well-worn. The waterwheel is not working; it was probably stopped for the photograph to be taken. The mill looks well-kept.

Liskeard
Looe Mill 1906 56322
The mill is a stone building with
half-hipped slate roof. The stone
bridge over the Looe River where
the children are gathered is on
the old main road. The mill is now
converted to a private house.

Rottingdean, From the Windmill c1965 R62037

Launceston, The Old Water Mill c1960 L20044

Launceston
The Old Water Mill c1960
This stone building with a slate roof and small brick chimney is on the River Tamar. It is powered by a narrow width low breastshot waterwheel.

Lynton
Lynbridge Mill 1900
This was a corn mill which was also used as a sawmill on the River Lyn. It is a brick building with a slate roof; it was powered by an overshot waterwheel until 1889, and then a turbine was installed in 1890. The waterwheel has probably been stopped for the photograph to be taken - hence the cascade of water from the by-pass sluice. The mill was destroyed by a devastating flood in 1952, and now only ruins are on the site.

Lynton, Lynbridge Mill 1900 45657

▼ **Maiden Newton, The Mill 1906** 54570
The mill is set on the River Frome, which flows into Poole Harbour;
it is a brick building, and is powered by a breastshot waterwheel. It is
now converted to a private house and business.

▼ **Mawgan, Lawreys Mill 1887** 20302
The two buildings on the Helford River, stone with slate roofs, have
overshot waterwheels. The house looks neat and well-kept.

▲ **Newquay
Trewerry Mill 1907**
59351
Trewerry Mill is on the
River Gannel, and is
a stone building with
carved stonework
and a slate roof. It is
powered by a backshot
waterwheel, which can
just be seen at the side
of the mill building, in the
centre of the picture.
It is now a guest house
and teagarden.

◄ **Penzance, The Old Mill Lamorna 1903** 50863
Bossava Mill is a small stone-built country corn mill with a slate roof. An overshot waterwheel powered just one pair of millstones, mounted on a hursting, through one step of primitive gearing. The mill is pictured when it was still in working order. This was a primitive and historic mill, which worked until 1919. It is now empty of all machinery and converted to a shop.

◄ **Polzeath**
Shilla Mill c1955
P705006
Shilla Mill, a stone
building with slate roof,
stands on small stream
flowing to the Atlantic
Ocean. The ornament in
the garden is possibly a
ship's figurehead. The
mill has been converted
into a private house.

◀ **Polperro**
Crumplehorn Mill 1908
59751
Crumplehorn Mill is a stone building with a slate roof, and is powered by an overshot waterwheel. It is a very visible mill, sited near the main car park in a busy holiday resort. It is now converted as part of a public house, with the waterwheel turning.

▼ **Port Isaac**
The Mill 1920 69691
On a small stream flowing to the Atlantic Ocean, the mill is a stone building with a slate roof. It is powered by an iron overshot waterwheel, which looks as if it is disused. The footpath down past the mill is well-used and clear of undergrowth.

◀ **Ruan Minor**
Poltesco Old Mill
1911 64003
This mill is now under restoration. Standing on a small stream flowing to the English Channel it is a stone building with a slate roof.

Salisbury, The Old Mill c1955 S48161
West Harnham Mill is a fine brick building with stone details and a tiled roof. Now empty of all machinery, and used as a shop and tearoom, it stands on the River Nadder, a tributary of the River Avon.

Witchampton, The Mill 1904 52742
This large mill of mixed construction is on the River Allen, which flows into the River Stour. An undershot waterwheel is located to the side of the building. The photograph shows the mill when it was still in full working order; it ceased work in 1931.

Scotland

Braemar
The Mill on the Clunie 1890 B266002
The mill is in the Cairngorms, set on the Clunie Water, which flows
into the River Dee. It is a stone building on a very rocky highland
river riverbank, and is powered by a breast shot waterwheel.

Killin
The Mill on the Dochart 1890 K51004
The mill, a stone building with a slate roof, stands near Finlarig
Castle on the River Dochart, which flows into Loch Tay. The natural
rocks on the river bed form an effective dam to feed the breast shot
waterwheel which was not working at the time of the photograph, so
the by-pass sluice is open. Tree trunks wait in the mill yard, indicating
that at least part of the mill trade was sawing timber.

Wales

Beddgelert, Gwynant Valley Mill 1889 21840
Old Nant Mill stands in the mountains by a very rocky river, the River Glaslyn, in the Nant Gwynant Valley, which is in the National Forest Park near Mount Snowdon. A stone building with slate roof, it is powered by a low breastshot waterwheel. The waterwheel is stopped, so the by-pass sluice is open and the water gushes into the rocky river.

Caergwrle, The Mill c1955 C363020
We are in the Welsh borders near Wrexham, on the River Alun, which flows into the River Dee. The mill is a stone building with a slate roof, and is powered by a breastshot waterwheel. The mill is in a range of buildings of differing construction and dates.

▼ **Erbistock, The Mill c1965** E121003
Again, this is Welsh border country on the River Dee. The mill is
a stone building with a slate roof, powered by a low breastshot
waterwheel. The milldam across the river is artificial; it is constructed
of stone piled in the river.

▼ **Ffynnongroew, Garth Mills c1955** F119006
The mill stands on the estuary coast of the River Dee; it is a stone
building with a slate roof. The height of water in the headrace is well
above the middle floor level of the mill, and half-way up the roof level
of the attached house. Let us hope that the dam does not leak!

▲ **Gumfreston
The Water Mill 1890**
28104
Gumfreston Mill is near
Tenby. A stone building
with a tiled roof, it looks
in poor condition. The
waterwheel appears to
have gone; the dark mark
on the wall shows where
it was located. The mill
was probably disused
at the time it was
photographed.

Llanbedr
Old Gwynfryn Mill 1889
21762
We are on Cardigan Bay, near Harlech. The mill, a stone building with a slate roof covered in ivy, is powered by a clasp-armed backshot waterwheel. The photograph shows that although the mill building is in poor condition, the waterwheel is in good working order. It looks as if the chimney at the front of the mill is discharging clear flue gases.

Monmouth, Monnow Mill 1914 67643
This mill on the River Monnow is a brick building with a slate roof, and is powered by a low breastshot waterwheel.

Rossett, The Mill 1895 36307
This picturesque mill, dated 1661, has distinctive regional building features of black and white half-timbering with brick infill. Powered by a low breastshot waterwheel, it stands on the River Alyn, a tributary of the River Dee. Now partly converted to a private house, and conserved in workable order, it is open to visit by prior appointment.

Isle of Man

Laxey
The Wheel 1894 33829
The Lady Isabella Waterwheel is a large 72-foot diameter backshot waterwheel; it was built in 1854,
and was used until 1929 for pumping water to drain lead mines. It stands on the Mooar Water, which
flows into the Laxey River. It is conserved, and turned as a showpiece for visitors.

Glossary of Terms

BACKSHOT
Type of waterwheel using reversed flow and gravity effect of water. Efficient type.

BREASTSHOT
Type of waterwheel using velocity and gravity effect of water. Efficient type.

HEADRACE
Watercourse directing water to a waterwheel or turbine.

HURSTING
Table-like structure on which millstones are mounted.

LUCAM
Hoistway for externally loading materials from ground level upward into a mill.

LANTERN
Structure at roof level at the top of an internal sack hoist way, for facilitating loading grain.

MILLSTONE
Flat cylindrical stones, used in pairs, mounted horizontally with one fixed and the other rotating. Grinding takes place between fixed and rotating flat faces. Speed is about 120 revolutions per minute.

OVERSHOT
Type of waterwheel using gravity effect of water. Most efficient type.

POST MILL
Type of windmill where the whole box body is mounted about a central pivot post.

ROLLER MILL
Steel rollers, mounted horizontally in pairs, rotating at slightly different speeds, mill the grain passed between them to reduce it to flour.

SCOOPWHEEL
Type of water-lifting waterwheel, used for land drainage.

SMOCK MILL
Type of tower windmill having a tower that is mainly constructed of wood.

STAGING
Structure for facilitating access to windmill sails, and sometimes caps.

TAILRACE
Watercourse, taking water away from a waterwheel or turbine.

TOWER MILL
Type of tower windmill having a tower that is constructed of brick or stone.

TRESTLE
Lower post supporting structure of a post mill.

TURBINE
Rotary water engine using velocity and gravity effect of water.

UNDERSHOT
Type of waterwheel using velocity and some gravity effect of water. Least efficient type.

Index

www.francisfrith.co.uk

The Francis Frith Collection publishes over 100 new titles each year. A selection of those currently available is listed below. For latest catalogue please contact The Francis Frith Collection. **Town Books** 96 pages, approximately 75 photos. **County and Themed Books** 128 pages, approximately 135 photos (unless specified). Pocket Albums are miniature editions of Frith local history books 128 pages, approximately 95 photos.

Accrington Old and New
Alderley Edge and Wilmslow
Amersham, Chesham and Rickmansworth
Andover
Around Abergavenny
Around Alton
Aylesbury
Barnstaple
Bedford
Bedfordshire
Berkshire Living Memories
Berkshire Pocket Album
Blackpool Pocket Album
Bognor Regis
Bournemouth
Bradford
Bridgend
Bridport
Brighton and Hove
Bristol
Buckinghamshire
Calne Living Memories
Camberley Pocket Album
Canterbury Cathedral
Cardiff Old and New
Chatham and the Medway Towns
Chelmsford
Chepstow Then and Now
Cheshire
Cheshire Living Memories
Chester
Chesterfield
Chigwell
Christchurch
Churches of East Cornwall
Clevedon
Clitheroe
Corby Living Memories
Cornish Coast
Cornwall Living Memories
Cotswold Living Memories
Cotswold Pocket Album
Coulsdon, Chipstead and Woodmanstern
County Durham
Cromer, Sheringham and Holt
Dartmoor Pocket Album
Derby
Derbyshire
Derbyshire Living Memories
Devon
Devon Churches
Dorchester

Dorset Coast Pocket Album
Dorset Living Memories
Dorset Villages
Down the Dart
Down the Severn
Down the Thames
Dunmow, Thaxted and Finchingfield
Durham
East Anglia Pocket Album
East Devon
East Grinstead
Edinburgh
Ely and The Fens
Essex Pocket Album
Essex Second Selection
Essex: The London Boroughs
Exeter
Exmoor
Falmouth
Farnborough, Fleet and Aldershot
Folkestone
Frome
Furness and Cartmel Peninsulas
Glamorgan
Glasgow
Glastonbury
Gloucester
Gloucestershire
Greater Manchester
Guildford
Hailsham
Hampshire
Harrogate
Hastings and Bexhill
Haywards Heath Living Memories
Heads of the Valleys
Heart of Lancashire Pocket Album
Helston
Herefordshire
Horsham
Humberside Pocket Album
Huntingdon, St Neots and St Ives
Hythe, Romney Marsh and Ashford
Ilfracombe
Ipswich Pocket Album
Isle of Wight
Isle of Wight Living Memories
King's Lynn
Kingston upon Thames
Lake District Pocket Album
Lancashire Living Memories
Lancashire Villages

Available from your local bookshop or from the publisher

The Francis Frith Collection Titles (continued)

Lancaster, Morecambe and Heysham Pocket Album
Leeds Pocket Album
Leicester
Leicestershire
Lincolnshire Living Memoires
Lincolnshire Pocket Album
Liverpool and Merseyside
London Pocket Album
Ludlow
Maidenhead
Maidstone
Malmesbury
Manchester Pocket Album
Marlborough
Matlock
Merseyside Living Memories
Nantwich and Crewe
New Forest
Newbury Living Memories
Newquay to St Ives
North Devon Living Memories
North London
North Wales
North Yorkshire
Northamptonshire
Northumberland
Northwich
Nottingham
Nottinghamshire Pocket Album
Oakham
Odiham Then and Now
Oxford Pocket Album
Oxfordshire
Padstow
Pembrokeshire
Penzance
Petersfield Then and Now
Plymouth
Poole and Sandbanks
Preston Pocket Album
Ramsgate Old and New
Reading Pocket Album
Redditch Living Memories
Redhill to Reigate
Richmond
Ringwood
Rochdale
Romford Pocket Album
Salisbury Pocket Album
Scotland
Scottish Castles
Sevenoaks and Tonbridge
Sheffield and South Yorkshire Pocket Album
Shropshire
Somerset
South Devon Coast
South Devon Living Memories
South East London
Southampton Pocket Album
Southend Pocket Album
Southport

Southwold to Aldeburgh
Stourbridge Living Memories
Stratford upon Avon
Stroud
Suffolk
Suffolk Pocket Album
Surrey Living Memories
Sussex
Sutton
Swanage and Purbeck
Swansea Pocket Album
Swindon Living Memories
Taunton
Teignmouth
Tenby and Saundersfoot
Tiverton
Torbay
Truro
Uppingham
Villages of Kent
Villages of Surrey
Villages of Sussex Pocket Album
Wakefield and the Five Towns Living Memories
Warrington
Warwick
Warwickshire Pocket Album
Wellingborough Living Memories
Wells
Welsh Castles
West Midlands Pocket Album
West Wiltshire Towns
West Yorkshire
Weston-super-Mare
Weymouth
Widnes and Runcorn
Wiltshire Churches
Wiltshire Living Memories
Wiltshire Pocket Album
Wimborne
Winchester Pocket Album
Windermere
Windsor
Wirral
Wokingham and Bracknell
Woodbridge
Worcester
Worcestershire
Worcestershire Living Memories
Wyre Forest
York Pocket Album
Yorkshire
Yorkshire Coastal Memories
Yorkshire Dales
Yorkshire Revisited

See Frith books on the internet at www.francisfrith.co.uk

FRITH PRODUCTS & SERVICES

Francis Frith would doubtless be pleased to know that the pioneering publishing venture he started in 1860 still continues today. Over a hundred and forty years later, The Francis Frith Collection continues in the same innovative tradition and is now one of the foremost publishers of vintage photographs in the world. Some of the current activities include:

Interior Decoration

Today Frith's photographs can be seen framed and as giant wall murals in thousands of pubs, restaurants, hotels, banks, retail stores and other public buildings throughout the country. In every case they enhance the unique local atmosphere of the places they depict and provide reminders of gentler days in an increasingly busy and frenetic world.

Product Promotions

Frith products are used by many major companies to promote the sales of their own products or to reinforce their own history and heritage. Frith promotions have been used by Hovis bread, Courage beers, Scots Porage Oats, Colman's mustard, Cadbury's foods, Mellow Birds coffee, Dunhill pipe tobacco, Guinness, and Bulmer's Cider.

Genealogy and Family History

As the interest in family history and roots grows world-wide, more and more people are turning to Frith's photographs of Great Britain for images of the towns, villages and streets where their ancestors lived; and, of course, photographs of the churches and chapels where their ancestors were christened, married and buried are an essential part of every genealogy tree and family album.

Frith Products

All Frith photographs are available Framed or just as Mounted Prints and Posters (size 23 x 16 inches). These may be ordered from the address below. From time to time other products - Address Books, Calendars, Table Mats, etc - are available.

The Internet

Already ninety thousand Frith photographs can be viewed and purchased on the internet through the Frith websites and a myriad of partner sites.

For more detailed information on Frith companies and products, look at these sites:

www.francisfrith.co.uk
www.francisfrith.com
(for North American visitors)

See the complete list of Frith Books at:

www.francisfrith.co.uk

This web site is regularly updated with the latest list of publications from The Francis Frith Collection. If you wish to buy books relating to another part of the country that your local bookshop does not stock, you may purchase on-line.

For further information, trade, or author enquiries please contact us at the address below:
The Francis Frith Collection, Frith's Barn, Teffont, Salisbury, Wiltshire, England SP3 5QP.
Tel: +44 (0)1722 716 376 Fax: +44 (0)1722 716 881   Email: sales@francisfrith.co.uk

See Frith books on the internet at www.francisfrith.co.uk

FREE PRINT OF YOUR CHOICE

Mounted Print
Overall size 14 x 11 inches (355 x 280mm)

Choose any Frith photograph in this book.
Simply complete the Voucher opposite and return it with your remittance for £2.25 (to cover postage and handling) and we will print the photograph of your choice in SEPIA (size 11 x 8 inches) and supply it in a cream mount with a burgundy rule line (overall size 14 x 11 inches).
Please note: photographs with a reference number starting with a "Z" are not Frith photographs and cannot be supplied under this offer.
Offer valid for delivery to one UK address only.

PLUS: Order additional Mounted Prints at HALF PRICE - £7.49 each (normally £14.99)
If you would like to order more Frith prints from this book, possibly as gifts for friends and family, you can buy them at half price (with no additional postage and handling costs).

PLUS: Have your Mounted Prints framed
For an extra £14.95 per print you can have your mounted print(s) framed in an elegant polished wood and gilt moulding, overall size 16 x 13 inches (no additional postage and handling required).

IMPORTANT!

These special prices are only available if you use this form to order. You must use the ORIGINAL VOUCHER on this page (no copies permitted). We can only despatch to one UK address. This offer cannot be combined with any other offer.

Send completed Voucher form to:
The Francis Frith Collection, Frith's Barn, Teffont, Salisbury, Wiltshire SP3 5QP

CHOOSE A PHOTOGRAPH FROM THIS BOOK

 *for* **FREE** *and Reduced Price Frith Prints*

Please do not photocopy this voucher. Only the original is valid, so please fill it in, cut it out and return it to us with your order.

Picture ref no	Page no	Qty	Mounted @ £7.49	Framed + £14.95	Total Cost £
		1	Free of charge*	£	£
			£7.49	£	£
			£7.49	£	£
			£7.49	£	£
			£7.49	£	£
			£7.49	£	£

Please allow 28 days for delivery.
Offer available to one UK address only

* Post & handling	£2.25
Total Order Cost	**£**

Title of this book . . . .

I enclose a cheque/postal order for £ . . . .
made payable to 'The Francis Frith Collection'

OR please debit my Mastercard / Visa / Maestro card, details below

Card Number

Issue No (Maestro only)   Valid from (Maestro)

Expires   Signature

Name Mr/Mrs/Ms . . . .
Address . . . .
. . . .
. . . .
. . . . Postcode . . . .
Daytime Tel No . . . .
Email . . . .

ISBN 0-7537-1404-3   Valid to 31/12/08

Can you help us with information about any of the Frith photographs in this book?

We are gradually compiling an historical record for each of the photographs in the Frith archive. It is always fascinating to find out the names of the people shown in the pictures, as well as insights into the shops, buildings and other features depicted.

If you recognize anyone in the photographs in this book, or if you have information not already included in the author's caption, do let us know. We would love to hear from you, and will try to publish it in future books or articles.

Our production team

Frith books are produced by a small dedicated team at offices in the converted Grade II listed 18th-century barn at Teffont near Salisbury, illustrated above. Most have worked with The Francis Frith Collection for many years. All have in common one quality: they have a passion for The Francis Frith Collection. The team is constantly expanding, but currently includes:

Andrew Alsop, Paul Baron, Jason Buck, John Buck, Heather Crisp, David Davies, Natalie Davis, Louis du Mont, Isobel Hall, Chris Hardwick, Lucy Hart, Julian Hight, Peter Horne, James Kinnear, Karen Kinnear, Tina Leary, Stuart Login, Sue Molloy, Miles Murray, Sarah Roberts, Kate Rotondetto, Dean Scource, Eliza Sackett, Terence Sackett, Sandra Sampson, Adrian Sanders, Sandra Sanger, Julia Skinner, Lewis Taylor, Shelley Tolcher, Lorraine Tuck, Miranda Tunnicliffe, Will Tunnicliffe, David Turner and Ricky Williams.